Tails with a Twist

Tails with a Twist

animal nonsense verse

LORD ALFRED DOUGLAS
Illustrated by Brian Robb

B.T. BATSFORD LTD. LONDON

First published 1979
© Edward Colman, the Douglas Literary Estate 1979

Set in 11 on 13 pt IBM Journal by Tek-Art Ltd
Printed by Butler & Tanner Ltd Frome, Somerset
for the Publishers B.T. Batsford Ltd,
4 Fitzhardinge Street, London W1H 0AH

ISBN 0 7134 1870 2

Contents

Preface

From the edition of 1928

I once wrote a book of pure nonsense; it was called *Tails with a Twist*, and achieved great successes, among them the flattering but (to me) not altogether satisfactory one of being very closely imitated by Mr. Hilaire Belloc, in a book which he called the *Bad Child's Book of Beasts*. This book actually appeared before *Tails with a Twist*, but most of the rhymes contained in my book had been written at least two years before Mr. Belloc's, and were widely known and quoted at Oxford, where Mr. Belloc was my contemporary, and in other places. I have no grievance against Mr. Belloc — as I have already said, his imitation of my rhymes was flattering, and legitimate — but as I have been constantly accused of plagiarising Mr. Belloc's rhymes, I take this opportunity of stating the exact facts. But to return to my point, these rhymes were pure nonsense rhymes. Those I have written since have become less and less purely nonsensical. Partly I regret it, partly I recognise that it is the inevitable result of the development which is inherent in every art. The desire to be more sophisticated and to show off technical accomplishment has gradually superseded the original devotion to what I still recognise as the higher form of nonsense. I claim for 'The Pongo Papers' and for 'The Placid Pug' that they are by far the most elaborate nonsense rhymes that have ever been attempted. I have devoted as much time and trouble and fundamental brain-work to their production as I have ever done to writing sonnets, and though I will not say they were as difficult to write as sonnets, I will say that they were very nearly as difficult. This is the excuse for their existence. If they were pure nonsense rhymes they would need no excuse. Being a hybrid article they need the excuse of elaborate technical perfection to justify them.

The Sword-Fish

The Sword-fish is an awful brute,
He tears your hair out by the root.

And when you're bathing in the sea,
He leaps upon you suddenly.

And if you get out on the sand,
He sometimes follows you inland.

The Hyæna

A curious beast is the Hyæna,
He has a very strange demeanour.

He seems at first quite free from guile,
And has a very winning smile.

And yet he often bites so much,
That you are forced to use a crutch.

It really does you good to hear
His laughter ringing loud and clear.

But when he bites your leg in half,
You don't feel much inclined to laugh.

The Rabbit

The Rabbit has an evil mind,
Although he looks so good and kind.

His life is a complete disgrace
Although he has so soft a face.

I hardly like to let you know
How far his wickedness will go.

Enough, if this poor rhyme declares
His fearful cruelty to hares.

He does his very best to keep
These gentle animals from sleep,

By joining in with noisy throngs
Of rabbits singing ribald songs.

To wake their fears and make them bound,
He simulates the Basset-hound.

And if he meets them after dark,
He imitates the greyhound's bark.

The Antelope

If you go out alone, I hope
You will not meet the Antelope.

No other beast is half so vicious,
So false, so cruel, so malicious.

It would be wrong for me to write
The sort of things he does at night.

Nor dare I in plain language say
The sort of things he does by day.

His acts recall, they are so serious,
Those of the Emperor Tiberius.

The Elephant

The Elephant is very wise,
Although he has such tiny eyes.

He is as agile as a pig,
Although he is so very big.

His voice is tuneful as a gong,
Although it is so very strong.

And though he has such frightful tusks,
He lives entirely on rusks.

His size, as you may easily think,
Demands a great amount of drink.

And yet he never once gets drunk,
Although he has so large a trunk.

His life is upright and erect,
And claims unanimous respect.

No beast with him can well compare,
Except, of course, the Belgian hare.

The Panther

The Panther is a perfect pest,
He gives you not a moment's rest.

From early morn till late at night
He keeps you in perpetual fright.

If you forget to shut the door,
He leaps upon you with a roar.

And when you're sitting at your meals,
He comes and snarls behind your heels.

The Baboon

The Baboon is a fearful ape,
From him there's really no escape.

The highest tree, the deepest cave,
From him is powerless to save.

Although his form you may not see,
He drops upon you from a tree.

And if his way your footsteps tend,
It practically means the end.

The Hen

The Hen is a ferocious fowl,
She pecks you till she makes you howl.

And all the time she flaps her wings,
And says the most insulting things.

And when you try to take her eggs,
She bites large pieces from your legs.

The only safe way to get these,
Is to creep on your hands and knees.

In the meanwhile a friend must hide,
And jump out on the other side.

And then you snatch the eggs and run,
While she pursues the other one.

The difficulty is, to find
A trusty friend who will not mind.

The Gazelle

A nasty beast is the Gazelle,
Unless you know him very well.

For if you're walking in the snow,
He comes and treads upon your toe.

And if you're walking in the wind,
He springs upon you from behind.

And if you're walking in the rain,
He really gives you fearful pain.

But if you always dress in white,
The chances are he'll be all right.

The Lion

The Lion is an awful bore,
He comes and dabbles in your gore.

And if he wants to have a feed,
He bites your leg and makes it bleed.

Although the tears stream from your eyes,
He takes no notice of your cries.

In vain you argue or protest,
He finishes his meal with zest.

Nor will he take the least rebuff
Until he feels he's had enough.

The Crocodile

A nice beast is the crocodile,
He has a very pleasant smile.

He's always ready with his jaws
In any really useful cause.

If in the Nile you take a swim,
You need not be afraid of him.

And if your strength should chance to fail,
He will assist you with his tail.

He lives entirely on fruits,
On oats, on mushrooms, and on roots.

The Viper

The Viper is a sickening snake,
He comes when you are not awake.

During the day-time he's all right,
But then he always comes by night.

He's quite innocuous by day,
But that's the time he keeps away.

He has a very stealthy creep,
He comes when you are fast asleep.

Say what you will, do what you like,
He's ultimately sure to strike.

His perseverance is immense,
The pain he causes is intense.

The Zebra

The Zebra is a perfect jewel,
In Winter he will fetch your fuel.

In Summer, when the heat is strong,
He comes and fans you all day long.

In Spring, when all the birds rejoice,
The woods re-echo with his voice.

In Autumn, when the north winds shout,
His splendid qualities come out.

In every corner of the earth
Men recognise his sterling worth.

The Eagle

The Eagle is a fearful bird,
He takes your eye without a word.

And when you're lying in your bed,
He whets his talons on your head.

And if you move or scream or start,
He drives his beak into your heart.

To cause pain is his only care:
How different from the Belgian hare!

The Shark

A treacherous monster is the Shark,
He never makes the least remark.

And when he sees you on the sand,
He doesn't seem to want to land.

He watches you take off your clothes,
And not the least excitement shows.

His eyes do not grow bright or roll,
He has astounding self-control.

He waits till you are quite undrest,
And seems to take no interest.

And when towards the sea you leap,
He looks as if he were asleep.

But when you once get in his range,
His whole demeanour seems to change.

He throws his body right about,
And his true character comes out.

It's no use crying or appealing,
He seems to lose all decent feeling.

After this warning you will wish
To keep clear of this treacherous fish.

His back is black, his stomach white,
He has a very dangerous bite.

The Pheasant

Few birds or beasts are more unpleasant,
Or more malicious, than the Pheasant.

For when the wind is in the East
He makes himself a perfect beast.

And when the wind is in the West
He makes himself a perfect pest.

All day he's very cross and bad,
And in the night he goes quite mad.

And even in the noonday heat
He's not a pleasant bird to meet.

If you should go out dressed in green,
He's pretty sure to make a scene.

And if you go out dressed in red,
It nearly sends him off his head.

In fact, all kinds and cuts of clothes
He equally abhors and loathes.

But if you wear no clothes at all,
Be ready for a funeral.

The Weasel

The Weasel is a perfect dear,
He'll never give you cause to fear.

If you walk out on a fine day,
He bounds before you all the way.

And if your boots are rather tight,
He bites them till they fit all right.

The Whale

When you are swimming do not fail
To keep a look-out for the Whale!

He has a most annoying knack
Of taking children on his back.

And when he's picked up two or three,
He whisks them off right out to sea.

Of course, at first you think it charming,
But very soon it gets alarming.

For when you say you'd like to land,
He doesn't seem to understand.

The more you beg him to go home,
The more he dashes through the foam.

He rushes on, mile after mile,
And lands you in some desert isle.

And there, until some ship appears,
You often have to stay for years.

The Ferret

There is one animal of merit
And perfect honesty: the Ferret.

I have not time to tell to you
The numerous things that he will do.

For if you do not overtask him,
He will do anything you ask him.

He is as clever as a pike,
He will do anything you like.

He is as faithful as a bear,
And gentle as a Belgian hare.

He is as strong as any fish,
He will do anything you wish:

Bite holes in leaves, tie knots in string,
Or practically anything.

The Leopard

The Leopard always seems to feel
That he is ready for a meal,

Although he mostly comes by night
To satisfy his appetite.

And you will quickly guess, I think,
The things he likes to eat and drink.

He really is a dreadful trial,
He never takes the least denial.

And if you're out when he should call,
He waits for hours in the hall.

He is a very hungry beast,
And always ready for a feast.

The Giraffe[*]

A doubtful friend is the Giraffe,
Distrust him when you hear him laugh.

He laughs like people at a ball,
And not because he's pleased at all.

He stretches out his neck like tape,
Until its length precludes escape.

And then he dexterously throws
The window open with his nose.

And if you hide beneath a chair
He finds you out, and pins you there.

* Written by the late Right Hon. George Wyndham, M.P.

40

41

42

The Ostrich

The Ostrich always seems to try
If he can peck you in the eye.

And if he can't succeed in that,
He gives a kick and knocks you flat.

And when he's rolled you in the mud,
He eats your flesh and laps your blood.

About this bird there's one good thing,—
He never hits you with his wing.

And he is very easily pleased
When once his appetite's appeased.

The Polar Bear

It's always well to take great care
Not to annoy the Polar Bear.

For though he's usually quite calm,
When roused he may do serious harm.

And though his nature's good and sage,
He's liable to fits of rage.

And when he's in these angry fits,
He sometimes tears you all to bits.

And then, when all the harm is done,
He's just as grieved as anyone.

Indeed, his eyes are often wet
With tears of genuine regret.

The difficulty is, to know
What are the things that rouse him so.

For though you try your best to please him,
The least thing sometimes seems to tease him.

And then, when once he's really nettled,
The whole thing's very quickly settled.

I have no doubt that you will say:
"Then why not keep out of his way?"

But that's the worst part of the case,—
He simply loves the human race.

And so, whatever you may do
To keep away, *he* comes to *you*.

46

The Albatross

The Albatross is most unfair,
He hurts you more than you can bear.

He does you really serious harm,
When he can get you on the arm.

And if he gets you on the hand,
It's simply more than you can stand.

If from his beak you get a poke,
You'll find it goes beyond a joke.

And if he hits you with his wing,
It is a very serious thing.

He is a nasty, dangerous brute,
He mostly gets you on the foot.

The Tiger*

The Tiger never seems to know
Where he may be allowed to go.

When little children say their prayers,
They hear him padding up the stairs.

When other people are in bed,
He roams about the room instead:

And if you wake and strike a light,
Resents this action with a bite.

And if you try and call your nurse,
It only makes the matter worse.

*Written by the Right Hon. George Wyndham, M.P.

The Blood-Hound

The Blood-hound is an awful pest,
He never gives you any rest.

In vain you try to get away,
He follows you both night and day.

He doesn't run so very fast,
But still he wears you down at last.

And so, however far you wend,
He always gets you in the end.

The Duck

I hope you may have better luck
Than to be bitten by the Duck.

This bird is generally tame,
But he is dangerous all the same;

And though he looks so small and weak,
He has a very powerful beak.

Between the hours of twelve and two
You never know what he may do.

And sometimes he plays awkward tricks
From half-past four to half-past six.

And any hour of the day
It's best to keep out of his way.

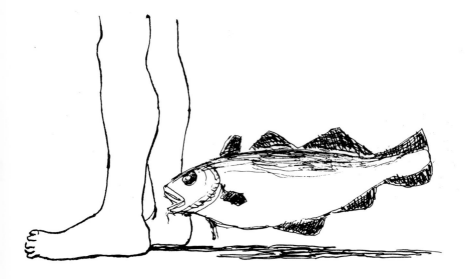

The Cod

There's something very strange and odd
About the habits of the Cod.

For when you're swimming in the sea,
He sometimes bites you on the knee.

And though his bites are not past healing,
It is a most unpleasant feeling.

And when you're diving down below,
He often nips you on the toe.

And though he doesn't hurt you much,
He has a disagreeable touch.

There's one thing to be said for him,—
It is a treat to see him swim.

But though he swims in graceful curves,
He rather gets upon your nerves.

The Placid Pug

The placid Pug that paces in the Park,
    Harnessed in silk and led by leathern lead,
Lives his dull life, and recks not of the Shark
    In distant waters. Lapped in sloth and greed,
He fails in strenuous life to make a mark,
The placid Pug that paces in the park.

Round the slow circle of his nights and days
    His life revolves in calm monotony.
Not unsusceptible to casual praise,
    And mildly moved by the approach of "tea,"
No forked and jagged lightning leaps and plays
Round the slow circle of his nights and days.

He scarcely turns his round protuberant eyes,
    To mark the mood of animals or men.
His joy is limited to mild surmise
    When a new biscuit swims into his ken.
And when athwart his gaze a Rabbit flies,
He scarcely turns his round protuberant eyes.

And all the while the Shark in Southern seas
   Pursues the paths of his pulsating quest,
Though the thermometer at fierce degrees
   Might well admonish him to take a rest,—
The Pug at home snores in ignoble ease.
(And all the while the Shark in Southern seas!)

If Pugs like Sharks were brought up in the sea
   And forced to swim long miles to find their food,
Tutored to front the Hake's hostility,
   And beard the Lobster in his dangerous mood,
Would not their lives more sane, more useful be,
If Pugs like Sharks were brought up in the sea?

The placid Pug still paces in the park,
   Untouched by thoughts of all that might have been,
Undreaming that he might have steered his bark
   Through many a stirring sight and stormy scene.
But being born a Pug and not a Shark
The placid Pug still paces in the park.

Song for Vintners

The Lion laps the limpid lake,
   The Pard refuses wine,
The sinuous Lizard and the Snake,
   The petulant Porcupine,
Agree in this, their thirst to quench
Only with Nature's natural "drench".

In vain with beer you tempt the Deer,
   Or lure the Marmozet;
The early morning Chanticleer,
   The painted Parroquet,
Alike, on claret and champagne
Gaze with unfaltering disdain.

No ale or spirit tempts the Ferret,
   No juice of grape the Toad.
In vain towards the "Harp and Merit"
   The patient Ox you goad;
Not his in rapture to extol
The praises of the flowing bowl.

The silent Spider laughs at cider,
   The Horse despises port;
The Crocodile (whose mouth is wider
   Than any other sort)
Prefers the waters of the Nile
To any of a stronger style.

The Rabbit knows no "private bar,"
   The Pelican will wander
Through arid plains of Kandahar,
   Nor ever pause to ponder
Whether in that infernal clime
The clocks converge to "closing time."

True "bona-fide traveller"
   Urging no sophist plea,
How terrible must seem to her
   Man's inebriety;
She who in thirsty moments places
Her simple trust in green oases.

With what calm scorn the Unicorn,
   In his remote retreat,
Must contemplate the fervour born
   Of old Château Lafitte.
Conceive the feelings of the Sphinx
Confronted with Columbian drinks!

Song for Sidlers

The Crab walks sideways, not because his build
   Precludes the possibility of walking straight,
And not (as some have thought) that he is filled
   With strange and lawless theories on gait;
Still less that he is foolishly self-willed
   And prone to show off or exaggerate.

No serious student of his life and ways
   Will venture to impugn his common sense;
His tact and moderation win high praise
   Even from those whose faculties are dense
And blind to the false issues which they raise
   When they accuse him of malevolence.

"But, ah!" these shallow hide-bound pedants cry,
   "If to the Crab all virtues you concede,
If his intentions are not evil, why
   This sidelong walk,
   These flanking steps that lead
To no advancement of Humanity,
   No exaltation of the mortal breed?

"Why not go forward as the Sword-fish goes?
   Or move straight backward, like the jibbing Horse?
Why this absurd and pitiable pose
   That takes delight in any devious course?
Why this dislike to 'following the nose'
   Which all the best authorities endorse?"

Insensate fools. Swims not the Cod in curves?
  Does not the running Roebuck leap and bound?
If in his flight the Capercailzie swerves,
  Shall he be mocked by every Basset-hound
Who, having neither feathers, wings, nor nerves,
  Has not the pluck to rise up from the ground?

Peace, peace, the Crab adopts a sidelong walk,
  For reasons still impossible to see.
And if his pride permitted him to talk
  To anyone who did not do as he,
His instinct would be, probably, to balk
  The hopes of vulgar curiosity.

And while the schoolmen argue and discuss,
  And fill the air with "whats" and "whens," and "whys,"
And demonstrates as: thus, and thus, and thus,
  The crab will pulverise their theories,
And put an end to all this foolish fuss
  By walking sideways into Paradise.

Fragments for Philosophers

In the abysses of the ocean deeps,
    Fathoms removed from men and mortal strife,
The unexpectant Oyster smiles and sleeps
    Through the calm cycle of his peaceful life.

What though above his head the steamboat plies,
    And close at hand he hears the fume and fuss
Of the impetuous Halibut that flies
    The mad embraces of the Octopus.

Though the fierce tails of Whales like flails descend
    Upon the water lashed to furious foam,
And the Sea-serpents writhe and twist and bend
    All round the purlieus of his ocean home,

He still preserves his philosophic calm,
    His high detachment from material things,
And lays to his untroubled soul the balm
    Of that contentment oft denied to kings.

Not far off, on the shore, men fume and fret,
    And prowl and howl and postulate and preach,
The Baby bellows in the bassinet,
    And the Salvation Army on the beach.

The unsuccessful "Artist" of the "Halls"
  Has blacked his face with cork, and now he sings
Of moon and coons and comic funerals
  And the enchantment that the cake-walk brings.

And on the pier the "milingtary band"
  Poisons the air with beastly brazen sound,
While Cockney couples wander hand in hand,
  And dismal tourists tour, and bounders bound.

And donkey-boys allure to donkey rides
  The sitters on the sand beside the sea,
And touts sell guides to all the town provides,
  From theatres to painless dentistry.

To all this noise the Oyster lends no ear,
   Partly because he has no ear to lend,
Partly because he hates to interfere,
   Chiefly because these rhymes must have an end.